This is dedicated to all parts of you.

The part of you that you once thought lost.
The part of you that feels angry.
The part of you that has been hurt.
The part of you that you once hated.
The part of you that can love beyond reason.
The part of you that lives in guilt.
The part of you that wanted it so badly.
The part of you that you couldn't let go of.
The part of you left wounded.
The part of you that struggles with forgiveness.
The part of you that wishes it never happened.
The part of you that understands it had to happen.
That part of you that no one saw.

This is for all of you.

-Lauren Carrión

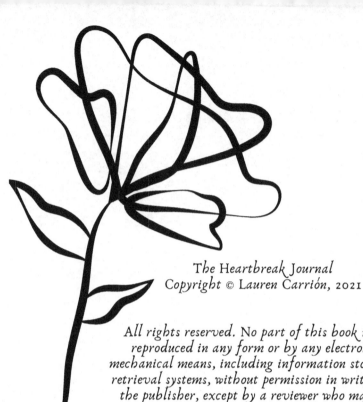

The Heartbreak Journal
Copyright © Lauren Carrión, 2021

ISBN- 978-0-578-86693-2

Dear Reader,

At one point or another, we all experience heartbreak. Our hearts can be broken by the death of a loved one, unimaginable betrayal, abandonment, severed friendship, or the end of a romantic or familial relationship. Being heartbroken is not just a metaphor. Having your heart broken causes undeniable distress and emotional pain. I once felt my heart muscles tearing away so slowly that it pained my chest as sadness and disappointment sunk deep into me. Broken heart syndrome is a documented medical condition that causes temporary disruption in our heart's pumping function and can cause chest pain and shortness of breath. That's right, the impact of heartbreak goes beyond that of emotional and mental distress; it also impacts your physical health. The good news is that the impact it has on your physical health can be reversible, and if ruptured heart vessels can heal, so can you.

Breakups can evoke emotions similar to grief due to the loss of connection and attachment to the projected future. It's not just your partner you are breaking up with. It's with the life, possibilities, dreams, investments, and hopes you created with your partner. The Kubler-Ross stages of grief include depression, denial, anger, bargaining, and acceptance. Heartbreak can also cause us to experience all of these stages, and yet breakups are so normalized that we often don't honor the grief they cause. For me, acceptance was deeper than finally acknowledging my relationship had ended. Acceptance was the beautiful aroma of peace and surrender that made me feel unafraid of love and connection.

After leaving a long-term relationship, I found myself feeling angry, resentful, sad, disconnected, and wanting to actively express my rage. At times, I felt so hurt and betrayed that I wanted nothing more than my ex to feel the wrath of my pain. Did I mention that I'm a therapist? If you thought being a therapist means you always make the most emotionally intelligent decisions for yourself, let me be honest and tell you it doesn't. As a therapist, I criticized myself for staying in my relationship past its shelf life. I found myself saying, "Lauren, you should have known better." Even though I acted on what I knew to be best at the time, my inner critic attempted to punish me for my past. Have you ever found yourself doing the same?

As a therapist, I've heard stories of love and loss, and I have also experienced them. I hope this journal will help you process your pain, encourage you to be gentle with yourself, and help you heal. Tennessee Williams once said, "We live in a perpetually burning building, and what we must save from it, all the time, is love." Let's begin with ourselves.

With love,

Lauren Carrión

HOW TO USE THIS JOURNAL:

OPEN IT

WRITE IN IT

LAUGH WITH IT

DRAW IN IT

CRY WITH IT

DON'T EDIT IT

TAKE YOUR TIME WITH IT

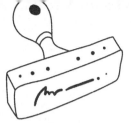

Today's Date:

Location:

time:

My current relationship status is...

My intention while using this journal is...

My mantra for healing through heartbreak will be...

HEARTBREAKS I'VE EXPERIENCED...

THE BREAK-UP IN ITSELF CAN BE A COMPLEX AND EMOTIONALLY CHARGED PROCESS. CAN YOU DESCRIBE THE JOURNEY LEADING UP TO YOUR BREAKUP? WAS IT ROCKY, SMOOTH, BRIEF, LENGTHY, CHAOTIC, AMICABLE, RESPECTFUL, ETC.?

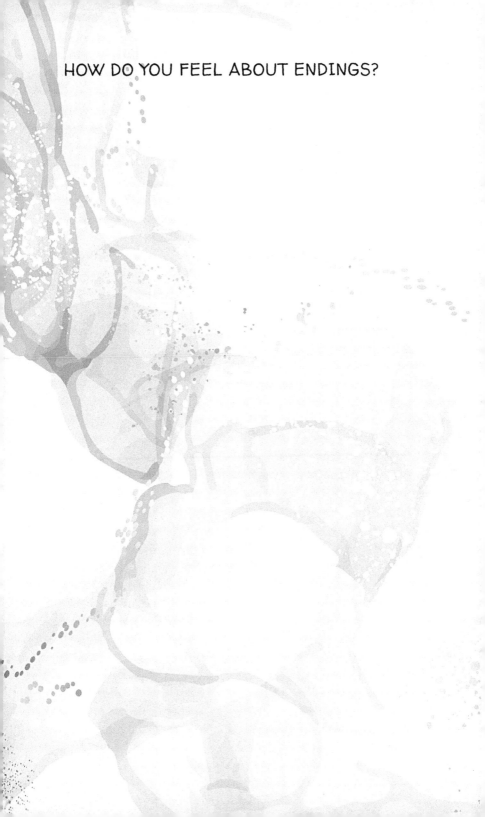

HOW DO YOU FEEL ABOUT ENDINGS?

HOW WOULD YOU DESCRIBE LOVE TO SOMEONE OUTSIDE OF THIS UNIVERSE?

SUPPORT AND CONNECTION ARE FUNDAMENTAL WHEN PROCESSING HEARTBREAK.

WRITE THE NAMES AND/OR DRAW THE PEOPLE YOU BELIEVE CAN SUPPORT YOUR HEALING JOURNEY.

WHO HURT YOU?

WHERE DO YOU FEEL THE PAIN?

DID YOUR RELATIONSHIP RUN THE COURSE
YOU EXPECTED IT TO? HOW WAS THE
REALITY OF YOUR RELATIONSHIP
ALIGNED OR MISALIGNED WITH
YOUR EXPECTATIONS?

HOW DID YOUR FAMILY,
CULTURE, COMMUNITY, OR
RELIGIOUS BELIEFS INFLUENCE
YOUR DECISION TO REMAIN
WITH OR LEAVE YOUR
PARTNER?

WHO MADE THE FINAL DECISION TO END YOUR RELATIONSHIP?
WAS IT A MUTUAL AGREEMENT?
HOW DOES WHO ENDED THE RELATIONSHIP IMPACT YOU?

HOW DID YOUR FAMILY AND FRIENDS REACT TO YOUR BREAKUP? HOW DID THEIR REACTIONS IMPACT YOU?

FILL IN THE TIMELINE BELOW WITH ANY IMPACTFUL EVENTS LEADING UP TO YOUR BREAKUP.

WHAT LONG-TERM IMPLICATIONS DID SPECIFIC EVENTS HAVE ON YOUR RELATIONSHIP?

When we feel hurt, we are more likely to use hurtful language or engage in hurtful behaviors towards those whom we love.

Did you do any of the hurting in your relationship?

HAVE YOU EVER HEALED FROM A
BREAKUP BEFORE? DESCRIBE
YOUR EXPERIENCE.

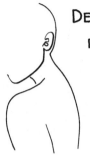

DESCRIBE YOUR ABILITY TO FOCUS ON
DAY-TO-DAY TASKS SINCE YOUR
BREAKUP.

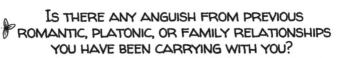

IS THERE ANY ANGUISH FROM PREVIOUS ROMANTIC, PLATONIC, OR FAMILY RELATIONSHIPS YOU HAVE BEEN CARRYING WITH YOU?

IF UNADDRESSED, WE CAN CONTINUOUSLY CARRY PAIN FROM FORMER FRIENDSHIPS, FAMILY, AND ROMANTIC PARTNERS WHO HAVE HURT US INTO OUR FUTURE.

HOW DOES IT FEEL
SLEEPING WITHOUT
YOUR PARTNER? DID
YOU SHARE A HOME
TOGETHER? DID YOU
HAVE ANY ROUTINES
YOU ARE NOW GETTING
USED TO COMPLETING
WITHOUT A PARTNER?

SLEEP IS PIVOTAL TO YOUR MENTAL, EMOTIONAL, AND PHYSICAL WELL-BEING. HOW WOULD YOU DESCRIBE YOUR CURRENT QUALITY OF SLEEP?

HERE IS AN EXAMPLE OF MY BEDTIME ROUTINE:

LIST YOUR BEDTIME ROUTINE BELOW:

Wash off stress in shower

Brush teeth

Moisturize skin

Review next day's schedule

Set alarm

Dim lights

Bedtime gratitude & prayer

HOW HAS YOUR LIFESTYLE BEEN IMPACTED BY THE END OF YOUR RELATIONSHIP?

DESCRIBE YOUR PARENTS' RELATIONSHIP.

ARE THERE ANY PARTS OF THEIR RELATIONSHIP THAT WOULD BE HEALTHY TO IMPLEMENT? ARE THERE ANY PARTS THAT WOULD BE HEALTHY TO RENOUNCE?

I FEEL MOST LOVED WHEN...

IS THERE A NEW ROLE THAT YOUR EX-PARTNER WILL PLAY IN YOUR LIFE?

SOME EXAMPLES INCLUDE EX-PARTNER, CO-PARENT, BUSINESS PARTNER, OR THERE CAN BE NO ASSIGNED ROLE FOR THEM IN YOUR NEW PRODUCTION.

HOW DO YOU CURRENTLY SPEND YOUR TIME? WHAT DO YOU WANT TO SPEND MORE TIME ON?

My examples of love have been...

I *have always wanted*...

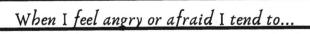

When I *feel angry* or *afraid* I tend to...

GRATITUDE LIST

RESEARCH SHOWS THAT
PRACTICING GRATITUDE REDUCES
STRESS, DEPRESSION, AND
INCREASES RESILIENCE.

WHAT ADVICE WOULD
YOU GIVE TO YOUR
DEAREST FRIENDS
GOING THROUGH A
BREAKUP?

WRITE
IT OUT!

IT'S NORMAL TO EXPERIENCE
LONELINESS AFTER A BREAKUP.
PERHAPS YOU ALWAYS WENT
GROCERY SHOPPING TOGETHER,
SPLIT YOUR MEALS, OR ENJOYED
THEIR EMBRACE AFTER A STRESSFUL
DAY.

WHAT DO YOU MISS THE MOST FROM
YOUR PARTNERSHIP?

PEOPLE HURTING US DOES NOT MEAN WE
DESERVE TO BE HURT.

PEOPLE LEAVING US DOES NOT MEAN WE
ARE DISPOSABLE.

HAVE YOU COME TO ACCEPT ANY BELIEFS THAT
IMPACT YOUR SELF-WORTH?

ACTIVITIES, EVENTS, & TRAVEL

IS THERE ANYTHING YOU'VE BEEN WANTING TO TRY BUT HAVE
CONTINUOUSLY DELAYED? THEN, LET'S PLAN FOR IT!

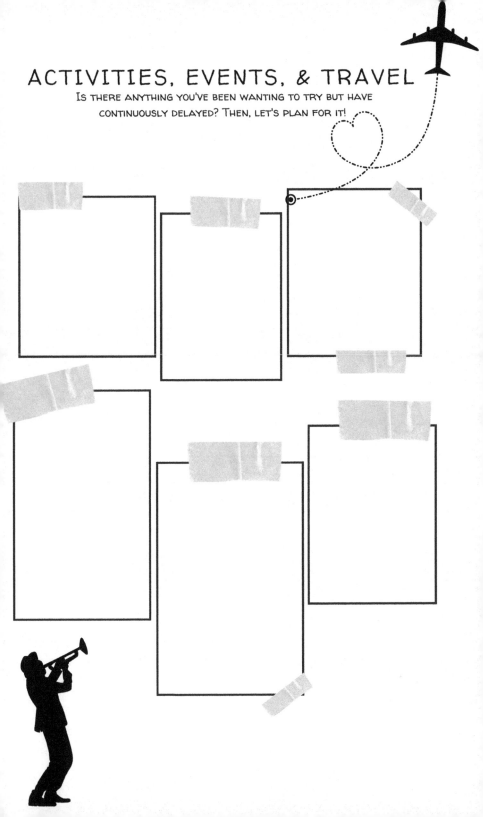

NAME A BREAKUP SONG THAT
SINGS TO YOUR HEART. WHICH
LYRICS RESONATE WITH YOU
THE MOST?
SING IT OUT LOUD!

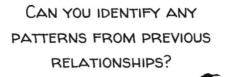

CAN YOU IDENTIFY ANY
PATTERNS FROM PREVIOUS
RELATIONSHIPS?

It's normal to feel sad when processing a breakup, and sometimes those sad feelings can turn into depression. However, be mindful that depression doesn't look the same for everyone. Symptoms can vary from mild to severe, and symptoms must last at least two weeks to be considered depression.

Listed below are some signs of depression:

- Constant fatigue
- Overeating or appetite loss
- Trouble concentrating
- Recurring thoughts of death
- Feelings of worthlessness
- Loss of interest & pleasure in things once pleasurable
- Sleep difficulties such as insomnia or sleeping too much
- Digestive problems that don't get better, even with treatment
- Persistent sad, anxious, or "empty" feelings
- Aches, pains, headaches, or cramps that won't go away
- Pessimism and hopelessness

There are several things people can do when feeling depressed. Connecting to an empathetic therapist who can help you process your emotions in a safe space can be healing and effective. The use of healthy coping skills and self-help techniques can also reduce symptoms and help improve your mood. I recognize it's not easy to start exercising if you are feeling constant fatigue, yet studies continue to show that regular exercise can reduce symptoms of depression. Eating healthy food, getting quality sleep regularly, spending time with loved ones, time in nature, and avoiding alcohol can also help.

WHAT KIND OF COPING SKILLS HAVE YOU BEEN USING TO MANAGE YOUR EMOTIONS?

AN EXAMPLE OF UNHEALTHY COPING SKILLS ARE OVER-EATING, DRINKING, DRUGS, ISOLATING YOURSELF, OVER SLEEPING, LASHING OUT, AND ENGAGING IN RISKY SEXUAL BEHAVIOR. THESE BEHAVIORS CAN FEEL HIGHLY SATISFYING AT THE MOMENT BUT THEY HAVE LONG TERM CONSEQUENCES.

AN EXAMPLE OF HEALTHY COPING SKILLS ARE EXERCISE, ARTISTIC EXPRESSION, QUALITY TIME WITH LOVED ONES, LEARNING NEW SKILLS, PARTICIPATING IN THERAPY, SPENDING TIME IN NATURE, JOURNALING, AND MUSIC.

USE THE BOXES BELOW TO IDENTIFY THE HEALTHY & UNHEALTHY COPING SKILLS YOU HAVE BEEN USING.

WHAT HEALTHY COPING SKILLS
WILL YOU COMMIT TO?

HOW ARE YOU GOING TO HOLD
YOURSELF ACCOUNTABLE?

HOW WILL YOUR COMMITMENT
TO YOURSELF CHANGE YOUR LIFE?

Yes, I can!

Yes, I can!

Yes, I can!

Yes, I can!

Yes, I can!

Yes, I can!

Yes, I can!

Yes, I can!

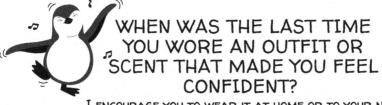

WHEN WAS THE LAST TIME YOU WORE AN OUTFIT OR SCENT THAT MADE YOU FEEL CONFIDENT?

I ENCOURAGE YOU TO WEAR IT AT HOME OR TO YOUR NEXT OUTING, AND WEAR IT FOR YOU!

WHAT CAUSED YOU TO SMILE INSTANTLY AS A CHILD?

WHEN WAS THE LAST TIME YOU DID SOMETHING SILLY ?

WHAT GAME DID YOU LOVE TO PLAY
AS A CHILD?

WHAT DID YOU SHARE TO BE YOUR FAVORITE COLOR WHEN YOU
WERE IN THE SECOND GRADE ?

WHAT ARE SOME OF THE ROLES YOU PLAYED IN YOUR RELATIONSHIP? E.G., BREADWINNER, CARETAKER, GUARDIAN, NURSE, WIFE, HUSBAND, HOMEMAKER.

WHEN WE OVER-IDENTIFY WITH ONE ROLE, WE TEND TO SUPPRESS THE OTHER PARTS THAT MAKE US SPECIAL.

TAKE THE TIME TO CLAIM WHO YOU ARE NOW.

WERE YOU CONNECTED TO ANYONE FROM
YOUR PARTNER'S LIFE THAT YOU NO
LONGER HAVE THE SAME ACCESS OR
CONNECTION TO?

E.G. FRIENDS, PETS, PARENTS, SIBLINGS, OR CHILDREN

YOUR BODY WORKS FOR YOU EVERY
SINGLE MINUTE OF EVERY DAY!
MASSAGE IT, PRAISE IT, FEED IT,
LOVE IT, AND EXERCISE IT!

CREATE A SCHEDULE BELOW LISTING HOW YOU
WILL TAKE CARE OF YOUR BODY THIS WEEK:

MONDAY

TUESDAY

WEDNESDAY

THURSDAY

FRIDAY

SATURDAY

SUNDAY

HOW DID YOU GROW FROM YOUR RELATIONSHIP? WHAT DID YOU LEARN ABOUT YOURSELF WHILE BEING WITH YOUR PARTNER? WHAT HAVE YOU LEARNED ABOUT YOURSELF WITHOUT A PARTNER?

WHOM WOULD YOU LIKE TO RECONNECT WITH NOW THAT YOU ARE SINGLE?

SOME EXAMPLES INCLUDE YOUR PASSIONS, SPIRITUALITY, FRIENDS, FAMILY, OR YOURSELF.

HAVE YOU EVER EXPERIENCED REJECTION? WHAT DID THAT REJECTION COME TO MEAN TO YOU?

Do you remember your very first crush? How did it feel? Whom did you tell?

What ignites your attraction to other people? Reflect on the interior and exterior attributes that genuinely captivate you. Have you prioritized either in your past relationships?

You get to choose who gets the privilege of being in your life. Take the time to reflect on the characteristics and values of people who are worthy of your time.

SET A TIMER AND WRITE FOR 5 MINUTES. DON'T STOP WRITING UNTIL THE TIMER ENDS.

CAN YOU LIST SOME WAYS IN WHICH YOUR
FORMER PARTNER HIGHLIGHTED SOME OF
YOUR BEST TRAITS? PROVIDE EXAMPLES. IF
YOU FEEL THAT YOUR PARTNER DIDN'T, HOW
DID THAT IMPACT YOU?

DO YOU FIND IT DIFFICULT TO TRUST PEOPLE?

HOW CAN YOUR TRUST BE EARNED?

ARE YOU HOLDING ONTO ANY
GRUDGES THAT WOULD BE
HEALTHIER FOR YOU TO
SURRENDER?

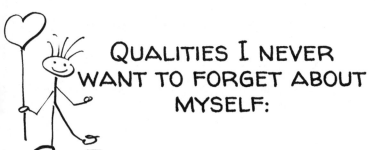

QUALITIES I NEVER WANT TO FORGET ABOUT MYSELF:

What does loneliness feel like for you? Have you been taught to believe that you are incomplete without a partner?

Do you keep any physical reminders of your ex?

This is a personal decision and there is no "right" answer. Whatever you choose, be sure to make room for your future self and for the person you want to enter your life.

Suggestion: Rotate a few items in your space to shift the energy in your home.

WHAT DO YOU WANT?

WHAT MAKES YOU FEEL HAPPY?

HAVE YOU BEEN TAUGHT TO DEPEND ON OTHER PEOPLE OR MATERIAL THINGS TO MAKE YOU FEEL HAPPY?

DO YOU FIND IT CHALLENGING TO ASK FOR HELP?

HAVE YOU ASKED ANYONE FOR SUPPORT ALONG YOUR JOURNEY?

IT'S NORMAL TO EXPERIENCE A RANGE OF EMOTIONS AFTER A RELATIONSHIP ENDS. SOME PEOPLE FEEL ANGRY AND DISCOURAGED ABOUT THE POSSIBILITY OF DEVELOPING NEW CONNECTIONS. WHICH OF THESE STATEMENTS DO YOU IDENTIFY WITH THE MOST?

EVERYONE SUCKS! THERE'S NO SUCH THING AS "TRUE LOVE," AND THE THOUGHT OF ROMANTIC GESTURES MAKES ME CRINGE.

MOST PEOPLE SUCK, KEEP THEM AWAY. I'M FOCUSED ON MYSELF AND ONLY MYSELF AND NO ONE ELSE.

I AM NEUTRAL ABOUT THE POSSIBILITY OF LOVE AND RECONNECTING WITH ANYONE.

I KNOW THERE ARE STRONG LOVE POSSIBILITIES AVAILABLE FOR ME, AND I AM HOPEFUL ABOUT FUTURE RELATIONSHIPS.

MY HEART IS OPEN TO LOVE, I TRUST MYSELF TO BE IN A HEALTHY, FULFILLING, AND COMMITTED RELATIONSHIP, AND I GIVE MYSELF OPPORTUNITIES TO CONNECT TO OTHERS.

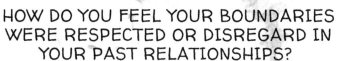

HOW DO YOU FEEL YOUR BOUNDARIES WERE RESPECTED OR DISREGARD IN YOUR PAST RELATIONSHIPS?

WHAT KIND OF HEALTHY BOUNDARIES
DO YOU BELIEVE ARE IMPORTANT TO
ESTABLISH IN FUTURE
CONNECTIONS?

IN WHAT WAYS DID YOUR PARTNER
ENCOURAGE OR DISCOURAGE YOU IN
ACTUALIZING YOUR LIFE GOALS?

WHAT DID YOU STOP DOING FOR YOURSELF BECAUSE OF YOUR RELATIONSHIP?

SOMETIMES PEOPLE QUIT HOBBIES, FRIENDS, OR
HABITS BECAUSE OF THEIR RELATIONSHIP.

WHAT DID YOU BELIEVE THAT YOU UNDERSTAND IS NO LONGER TRUE AND HAS NEVER BEEN TRUE?

PROVIDE EXAMPLES...

ARE THERE ANY WAYS IN WHICH YOU STOPPED TAKING CARE OF YOUR MENTAL, PHYSICAL, OR EMOTIONAL WELL-BEING WHILE BEING IN YOUR RELATIONSHIP? CAN YOU IMAGINE BEING WITH A PARTNER THAT ENCOURAGES YOU TO TAKE CARE OF YOURSELF AND WHO MAKES SELF-CARE PART OF YOUR RELATIONSHIP?

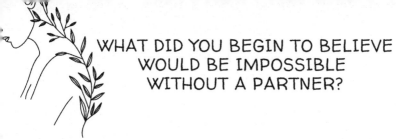

WHAT DID YOU BEGIN TO BELIEVE
WOULD BE IMPOSSIBLE
WITHOUT A PARTNER?

DO YOU FEEL ANY PRESSURE TO
GET INTO A RELATIONSHIP?

WHAT DO YOU FEAR THE MOST? WHAT IS THE SOURCE OF YOUR FEAR?

LET'S KICK ASS! WRITE ALL OF THE
UNHELPFUL THOUGHTS WE NEED TO
DESTROY AND REPLACE.

EXAMPLE: I AM NOT WORTHY OF LOVE
REPLACE: I AM WORTHY AND
DESERVING OF LOVE

HOW DOES YOUR BODY FEEL TODAY?
CAN YOU IDENTIFY WHERE IN THE
BODY YOU TEND TO
HOLD STRESS?

HOW DO YOU MANAGE DIFFICULT CONVERSATIONS?

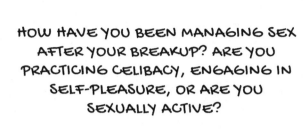

HOW HAVE YOU BEEN MANAGING SEX
AFTER YOUR BREAKUP? ARE YOU
PRACTICING CELIBACY, ENGAGING IN
SELF-PLEASURE, OR ARE YOU
SEXUALLY ACTIVE?

HOW DO YOU FEEL YOUR PREVIOUS PARTNER UNDERSTOOD OR MISUNDERSTOOD YOUR SEXUAL DESIRES?

WHAT KIND OF SEXUAL RELATIONSHIP DO YOU DESIRE WITH YOUR FUTURE PARTNER?

HOW WILL YOU COMMUNICATE YOUR NEEDS TO YOUR FUTURE PARTNER?

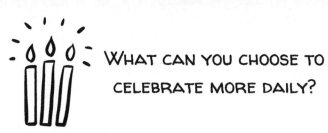

WHAT CAN YOU CHOOSE TO CELEBRATE MORE DAILY?

It's hard to admit, but sometimes I...

*Can you visualize the perfect
cuddle? What does it feel like?
What is the most comforting
part about it?*

I FORGIVE MYSELF FOR...

BURN THIS LETTER

TEAR HERE BEFORE BURNING. BE SURE TO FOLLOW FIRE SAFETY PROCEDURES

YOU ARE
VALUABLE AND
COMPLETE
WITHOUT A
PARTNER.

YOU ARE
VALUABLE AND
COMPLETE WITH
A PARTNER.

LOVE IS EVERYWHERE.
AS A THERAPIST, I HAVE FOUND THAT PEOPLE IN THE
HEALTHIEST RELATIONSHIPS DO NOT SOLELY RELY ON
THEIR PARTNER TO WATER THEIR STREAM OF LOVE,
BUT THEY ALSO RELY ON THEMSELVES AND THEIR
SUPPORT CIRCLE TO ADD TO THAT STREAM.

IDENTIFY THE SOURCES THAT WILL FEED YOUR RIVER.

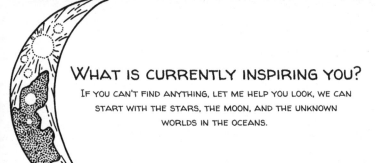

WHAT IS CURRENTLY INSPIRING YOU?

IF YOU CAN'T FIND ANYTHING, LET ME HELP YOU LOOK, WE CAN
START WITH THE STARS, THE MOON, AND THE UNKNOWN
WORLDS IN THE OCEANS.

HOW CAN YOU GROW FROM LOVING YOURSELF WHILE SINGLE?

WHAT DO YOU BELIEVE PEOPLE SEE WHEN THEY LOOK AT YOU?

WHAT DO YOU WANT PEOPLE TO SEE?

What qualities do you believe are most important for you future partner to have?

Consider how a partner can contribute to your emotional, physical, spiritual, and mental well-being.

VISUALIZE YOUR DREAM DATE.
HOW DO THEY LOOK AT YOU?
WHAT DO THEY SMELL LIKE?
WHERE ARE YOU?
WHAT DO YOU GET TO SHARE TOGETHER?
HOW DO THEY MAKE YOU FEEL?

ARE THERE ANY DIFFICULT
CONVERSATIONS YOU'VE BEEN
RUNNING AWAY FROM?

DESCRIBE EXPERIENCES YOU WOULD LIKE TO HAVE IN A FUTURE RELATIONSHIP.

IN MY NEW LOVE STORY...

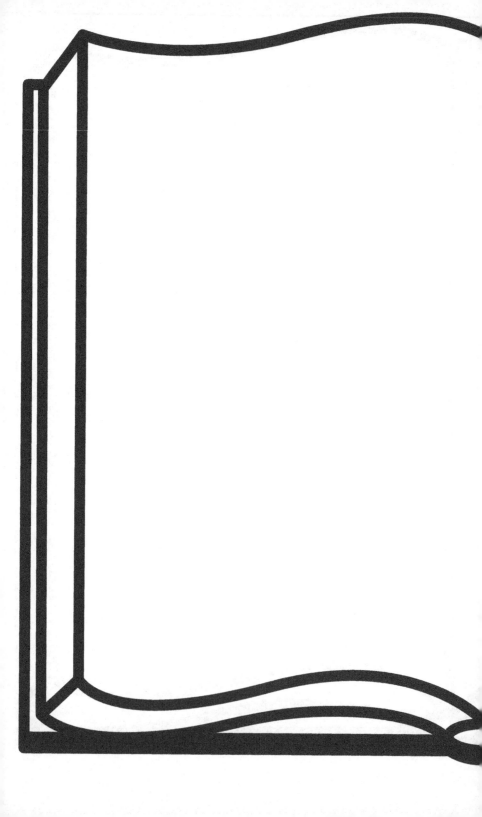

Emotional availability means being able to feel your way through challenging and uncomfortable emotions with yourself and others. Being emotionally available allows you to connect beyond the surface level and allows you to sustain an authentic emotional connection with others.

Sometimes we connect with someone and yet feel something is missing. It can be our lack of emotional availability or our partner's.

It's normal to be emotionally unavailable after a heartbreak; it's a response to pain and trauma, which can become a defense mechanism that prevents you from getting close to someone and thus keeps you feeling safe.

How can you identify when you are emotionally available?

TEN THINGS I LOVE ABOUT MYSELF

1.

2.

3.

4.

5.

6.

7.

8.

9.

10.

COMPASSION & COMMITMENT

How do those attributes contribute to a healthy and meaningful relationship to yourself and others?

After my breakup I...

CREATE YOUR RELATIONSHIP
NON—NEGOTIABLES:

I *have been taught to believe love is...*

I *now understand love is...*

WHAT CHARMS AND TALENTS
HAVE YOU BEEN KEEPING TO
YOURSELF THAT YOU WOULD
LIKE TO SHARE WITH THE
WORLD?

Today I unapologetically feel...

WHAT KEEPS YOU HOPEFUL?

IMAGINE YOUR BODY AS A STRONG & ANCHORED TREE.
VISUALIZE THE ROOTS THAT WILL KEEP YOU GROUNDED
& DECORATE YOUR BRANCHES WITH
PRAISES OF LOVE.

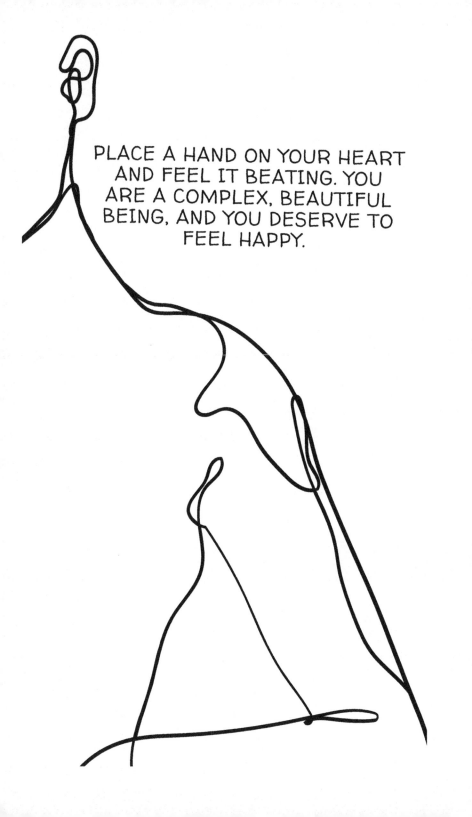

PLACE A HAND ON YOUR HEART
AND FEEL IT BEATING. YOU
ARE A COMPLEX, BEAUTIFUL
BEING, AND YOU DESERVE TO
FEEL HAPPY.

WRITE A LETTER FULL OF LOVE, DESIRES,
WISHES, AND AFFIRMATIONS TO YOURSELF.
FOLD IT AND OPEN IT 1 YEAR
FROM TODAY.

Congratulations!

You have officially completed the heartbreak journal!

You should feel proud of yourself for taking the time to complete these prompts and being intentional about your healing process. Healing from heartbreak can feel grueling, but it's not impossible! Connect with your support circle and invest in your well-being by committing to healthy habits even when you aren't up for it.

Remember that healing is a process, and it's normal to have moments that can open old wounds. Be mindful of your triggers so that they don't spill over into new experiences and new people. If you are experiencing frequent sadness, isolating yourself, or doubting your self-worth, consider reaching out to a therapist. There are some cool-ass therapists out there ready to support you, I promise!

Take a look back at your journal entries on difficult days and reflect on your answers. Are they the same? Have any of your feelings changed? Completing the final journal prompt does not define the end of this journey. So what's next for you? Whatever you choose for yourself, and there is power in that.

Go be your badass, sensational, courageous self!

With so much love,
Lauren Carrion

P.S. I would love to hear what you thought about this journal. Please write to me at officialheartbreakjournal@gmail.com.

Made in the USA
Las Vegas, NV
20 July 2021

26779621R00125